The best of Jeff & Maude

(and the rest of their Odd Squad!)

FOR VALENTINE'S DAY, JEFF GIVES MAUDE A GOLDEN SHOWER

PHEW!

by Allan Plenderleith

ℜℜ
RAVETTE PUBLISHING

For Becky,
my insPOOration.

The Odd Squad and all related characters © 2007
Created by Allan Plenderleith
www.allanplenderleith.com

First published in 2007 by
Ravette Publishing Limited
Unit 3, Tristar Centre, Star Road, Partridge Green,
West Sussex RH13 8RA

ISBN: 978-1-84161-294-2

In the beginning...

Here it is, the first ever Jeff cartoon. Rubbish, isn't it? But, for some reason this ugly little balding fat guy made me laugh and I wanted to do more. James became Jeff, and Tasty Morsels became The Odd Squad. Thankfully my standards became higher. Well, a bit.

Allan Plenderleith

The banana Jeff bought last week
had turned bad

It wasn't so much the poo in
his slipper that bothered Jeff —
more the smirk on his dog's face

Jeff enters a
'go for another wipe or leave it'
dilemma

Jeff had an annoying
hare in his mouth

Never sneeze while
squeezing toothpaste

Billy is about to stamp when he
feels a light tap on his shoulder

Never blow-off wearing a g-string

One dark evening, Jeff became a sad victim of the phantom head and bum swapper

Billy's biology lesson turns to the importance of jobby types

Jeff is outwitted by the aubergine

Jeff auditions for the little-known 'Excessive Body Hair Orchestra'

After repeated banging and a loud 'crack', Jeff's door finally closed

While on his way to the shops, Billy gets stung by a bee

Honey
£60 a jar

Having waited 17 hours after his 999 call, Jeff realised he'd actually called St. John's ambience

During the night, somebody had replaced Jeff's limbs with selected root vegetables

Someone had sharpened the strings on Jeff's guitar

Jeff's thug pellets seem to be working

Somehow, during the night, the tomatoes had moved from the vegetable basket to the fruit bowl

Billy and Moira carry out a hardness test on Cyril

Vicious traps, poison, mouldy cheese — clearly, this madman had to be stopped

Apparently no-one else could hear it — but Maude could — the cake was whispering: 'Lick the icing', 'Lick the icing'

Jeff is slightly confused when the waiter produces a large giraffe of wine

During the disco, Maude finds an embarrassing ladder in her tights

Although the survivors had no food and were miles from anywhere - they needn't worry- because Jeff had remembered the flares

Billy and Moira perform another
'don't try this at home kids' trick

The transition from girl to woman
is both sudden and disturbing

Just as her dream date walks in,
Maude's front-fastening bra simply snaps

Jeff plays that popular party game, 'Guess the Real Walnut Whirl'

Never underestimate a hamster

Billy's rabbit becomes the ill-fated star of a You've Been Framed clip

Jeff makes a cat flap

Maude looks up an old friend

One of Jeff's friends is a homosexual closet

Far from saggy boobs being a burden, they can become handy holders for cigarettes and pencils

For her birthday, Maude's boyfriend gives her multiple organisms

Jeff loves potato wedgies.

Jeff receives a large
Czech through the post.

Once again, Jeff had to work late because they were short-staffed.

Clearly, during the night, the dog had discovered how to operate the pencil sharpener.

Once again, Jeff was overdrawn.

As a louder and more satisfying alternative to clapping, Lily slaps together the loose skin under her arms.

Although they'd lost both wings, Dug brings the plane down safely with his 70's style lapels.

Maude had locked her shelf out again.

The morning after, Jeff's mouth felt like he'd licked a badger's arse.

Maude had a feeling it was time to trim her bikini line.

Once again, Alf spent the
night 'on the piss'.

In her retirement, Lily likes to make balloon
animals at children's parties.

Suddenly the burglar realised he wasn't the only fat person in the room with a big beard.

To make room for the beer for his party, Jeff had to get rid of a few things from the living room.

When the boss walked in, Maude was backing up her stuff on a floppy.

Fed up with birds splatting on his beloved car, Alf gains revenge.

Fortunately, having a boob job had not affected Maude's breastfeeding.

Suddenly Maude regretted the botox injections.

When Debbie got undressed, Dug discovered she had a 'Brazilian' down there.

Like many women of a certain age, Maude realised her bum had moved south.

No-one knew where the cork had gone - but
Camp Colin seemed suddenly cheerful.

You know you're getting on a bit when
your birthday cake needs a candle extension.

Jeff's home-made winter hot-tub for tiny helpless birds suddenly malfunctions.

Always forgetting her chip & pin number, Lily writes it down somewhere that no-one would look.

Lily had no idea her plain cookies were soon to be 'chocolate chip'.

On a flight, Jeff always looked forward to the complimentary nuts.

It was so cold that Alf could see
Lily's nipples.

After hours of endless tinkering,
Jeff finally makes his computer go faster.

Unfortunately, in the confusion and terror of being chased by a dog, Ginger had mistaken the air vent for the cat flap.

Jeff finally discovers something to stop his computer catching a virus.

Whenever Dug and his mates get drunk, they always do the 'congo'.

Suddenly Jeff discovers where the missing condoms had disappeared to.

Upon reflection, perhaps the best place for the dartboard wasn't beside an open window.

After listening to some hip-hop music, Billy spends the weekend in 'da hood'.

At the disco, Maude gets into a fight
with some dirty hoe.

The morning after, Jeff had a
disgusting film over his mouth.

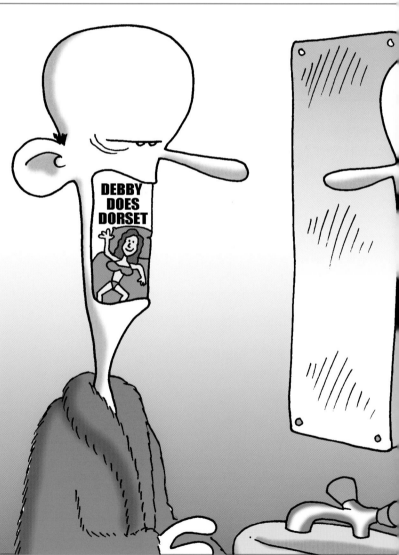

Moira couldn't decide what was more annoying - the fact the dog had eaten her homework or that he'd gotten it right.

Jeff is caught smuggling some dope through customs.

Unexpected but not unpleasant, during love making Barbara began tickling Dug's bum.

Billy invents a fun new game: 'spot the elderly squirrel'.

Suddenly, Lily decides to get a face wax.

Why it's a bad idea to visit your Nan just after a fancy dress party.

As he became older, Alf began to have trouble with his joints.

Dug's date with 'Barbara' was going great, until the taxi lights shone through her dress.

The dog was delighted - Jeff had left a meaty curry on the floor for him. AND it was warm!

During their footie match, the medic ran out with something for Dug's injury.

Dug was delighted to find the indian takeaway he ordered came with a free nan.

Dug was really into 'gangsta wrap'.

Jeff sat next to a man on the tube who gave him the willies.

Unfortunately during his golf game, Jeff's ball landed in a bit of rough.

Billy finally discovers where his good crayons had disappeared to.

Drunk Maude had forgotten to pull down her g-string before going for a sneaky poo.

Alf didn't have the heart to tell Lily that the new 'hamster' she had found in the bathroom was actually the soap.

For her birthday, Maude got a hands-free mobile.

As the embarrassed Jeff arrived at casualty, he realised he could now add 'envy' to his list of emotions.

Jeff likes to hang out with his mates down the pub.

During his long journey, Jeff decides to stop on the hard shoulder for a quick wee.

Not wishing to be seen scratching his itchy bum in public, Jeff simply uses the fire hydrant behind him.

Maude was horrified to discover Jeff's jazz mags under the bed.

Jeff spends another weekend getting lashed.

Maude walks in on Jeff while he was playing with himself.

Although the flower looked pretty it smelled surprisingly awful.

Judging by all the chocolate kisses on the floor, the dog's bum was in need of a wash again.

Lily didn't mind the kids playing with her knickers, if only they weren't using them as an aircraft hanger.

Maude had actually asked Jeff to put some Barry White on the stereo.

Having covered Jeff in chocolate sauce, Maude had got a bit carried away.

Maude's friend was a big slapper.

Once again, Billy's goldfish had diarrhoea.

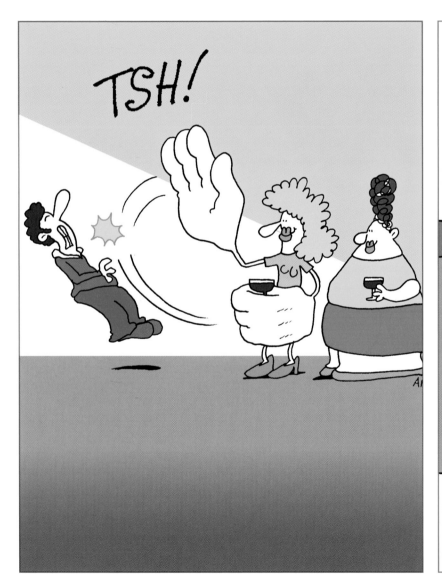

Jeff called round to see Maude, but unfortunately she had just popped out.

Men are still turned off by Maude's armpit hair, even when it's arranged in attractive plaits.

Unfortunately, Jeff's bogie flick did not go
in the intended direction.

When Jeff returned to his car,
there was a big bird dropping on it.

Apparently, the dog had swallowed
an icing bag nozzle again.

Jeff suddenly realises his flies were down.

When he has a pub lunch, Jeff always orders
chicken in a basque.

Just as Billy finished his poo,
the toilet paper ran out.

Jeff had mistakenly used volumising shampoo on the dog.

Jeff gives the illusion of a full head of brown curls by simply back-combing his bum hair.

Only when blowing up his new sex doll did Jeff realise he'd been given the wrong model.

Something told Jeff the kebab wasn't entirely made from lamb.

Never burp during a snog.

Jeff had a terrible feeling
the dog had worms.

At the end of their posh restaurant meal,
Maude has a dessert wine.

Having ran out of profilactics,
Jeff improvises.

Although the hamster had been depressed lately, Jeff had foolishly left him home alone with the spaghetti.

Suddenly, during her sexy dance, Maude's suspenders snap.

For some reason, Berty Big Nose always seemed to have two girlfriends.

After seeing Dave's method of frothing milk, Jeff decides to skip the cappuccino.

Billy hoped no-one would notice
he had terrible wind.

Unfortunately, the sock Dug had stuffed down his
trunks to look more manly had slipped.

To avoid getting pregnant, Dug had heard that before climax the man should withdraw.

For her birthday, Jeff surprises Maude with a slap-up meal.

Unfortunately Jeff and Maude only realised AFTER their frantic bonkathon, that the dog was under the bed.

Jeff's dog learns that humping the sofa is not without its consequences.

Never hug too hard if you've
put on baby oil.

Jeff makes sure he never gets another
pair of socks for Christmas.

Determined to get fit, Maude bought
a new pair of jogging bottoms.

Whilst out boozing, Dug and his mates
put their money in a kitty.

Normally, getting chatted up at the bar by a female dressed from head to toe in leather would be a good thing.

When he went out on the town, Dug always made sure his mobile was charged.

Jeff likes to impress
his workmates by using two
fake mannequin legs
and a pair of high heels.

Sadly, Maude's
impromptu 'booty shake'
had only succeeded in
dislodging a surprise
cling-on from within.

Maude decides to get rid of all the useless junk that cluttered up the living room.

On long journeys, Jeff always let the dog stick its head out of the window.

If he hasn't had sex in a while, Jeff simply spanks the monkey.

Whilst everyone else at the pottery class made vases and bowls, Jeff decided to make some attractive jugs.

Whilst giving the dog emergency mouth to mouth, Jeff mistakenly blows a bit too hard.

Why wait for NHS treatment when you have the internet!

Jeff loved onion rings.

Once again, the coffee machine
was out of order.

Jeff had the feeling his PC needed more memory.

During their game of tennis, everyone realised the ball was definitely <u>out</u>.

Jeff decides to ban pets from the bedroom.

At the nightclub, someone pinched
Maude's bum.

Maude was having difficulty potty training.

Jeff finally found a place for his remote control where no-one would touch it.

At the fabric shop, Lily asks the assistant for a sample.

Why older women should avoid going on roundabouts.

Jeff loved relaxing in the country listening to the calming sound of running water.

Maude's skirt was so short that when she bent over everyone saw her kebab.

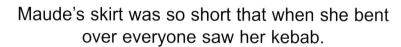

Dug's attempt at the old 'hole in the bottom of the popcorn box trick' suddenly backfires.

Jeff's dog discovers that trying to brake on newly polished laminate flooring is almost impossible.

Jeff reflected on how it seemed like only yesterday when their little son couldn't talk or walk for himself.

Maude learns why you should never take your nan out in the rain just after a perm and set.

Jeff and Maude visit the great sphincter of Egypt.

As Jeff turned on his computer he discovered it had been attacked by spam.

Who needs nipple tassles to do a sexy dance when you have excess nipple hair?

Jeff discovers the old 'string attached to a door handle' method is not the best way to remove a wobbly tooth.

Jeff knew his dog was healthy because he had lovely wet nose.

Unfortunately, Billy's plan to get closer to the ladies had failed.

Although in her thirties, Maude still got whistles from men in the street.

Maude finally discovers who was responsible for the skidmarks in the toilet bowl.

Clearly the cat had figured out how to work ebay.

The boss could tell Jeff had just been looking at internet porn.

The Hidden Vault!

Here they are. Having been locked away like shameful mutant children in an attic, they're finally free
- the dark, twisted and frankly disturbing cartoons which have never seen the light of day.
Until now! Don't have nightmares! Woo haa haa haaaa!

Alf discovers why you should never wear colostomy bags on high altitude flights

Jeff has never needed to buy dog food, not since he discovered the house had mice

Jeff was thoroughly enjoying his soup
when he discovered a cubic hair

Jeff finally decided to find out if
legend was true – were walnuts
in fact dried turtle brains?

To give the appearance of a firmer younger cleavage, Lily enlists the help of Bobo and Cheeko, the circus dwarves

Unfortunately, leaving the fish outside to 'see the snow' was not one of Billy's best ideas

Maude discovers why
'Flagpole Pete' was so called

Whenever Maude loses the tin opener
she simply employs the services of
the local buck-toothed child

Suddenly, Alf discovers why
Randy the clown came so cheap

Maude shook off the feeling she
was being watched, safe in the
knowledge she was 20 storeys high

On closer inspection, the dog did not
have rotting testicles — just a
couple of brussel sprouts stuck to his fur

Billy discovers that sometimes
you can hug too hard

Clearly
the ant killer
was working

Typical,
thought Billy.
His scary clown
mysteriously
springs to life
but not his
Mistress
Amazon doll

The school project to 'make an animal out of food items' hadn't quite gone as the teacher expected

As the fire was dying down, Alf asked Lily to chuck on some coal

Suddenly, Billy saw the horse
grow a fifth leg

Maude was in a dilemma - should she
or shouldn't she tell Jeff that her
cold sore had just dropped off

As Jeff entered the remote country pub, he had a feeling some of the locals were in-bread

Short-sighted Lily found her porridge really difficult to stir that morning

Complete your Odd Squad Collection!

Title		ISBN	Price
The Odd Squad's Disgusting Book for Boys	(hardcover)	978 184161 273 7	£7.99
The Odd Squad's Big Poo Handbook	(hardcover)	978 184161 168 6	£7.99
The Odd Squad's Sexy Sex Manual	(hardcover)	978 184161 220 1	£7.99
The Odd Squad Butt Naked		978 184161 190 7	£3.99
The Odd Squad Gross Out!		978 184161 219 5	£3.99
The Odd Squad's Saggy Bits		978 184161 218 8	£3.99
The REAL Kama Sutra		978 184161 103 7	£3.99
The Odd Squad Volume One		978 185304 936 1	£3.99
I Love Poo!	(hardcover)	978 184161 240 9	£4.99
I Love Sex!	(hardcover)	978 184161 241 6	£4.99
I Love Wine!	(hardcover)	978 184161 239 3	£4.99
I Love Beer!	(hardcover)	978 184161 238 6	£4.99
I Love Dad!	(hardcover)	978 184161 252 2	£4.99
I Love Mum!	(hardcover)	978 184161 249 2	£4.99
I Love Xmas!	(hardcover)	978 184161 262 1	£4.99
The Odd Squad's Little Book of Booze		978 184161 138 9	£2.99
The Odd Squad's Little Book of Men		978 184161 093 1	£2.99
The Odd Squad's Little Book of Oldies		978 184161 139 6	£2.99
The Odd Squad's Little Book of Poo		978 184161 096 2	£2.99
The Odd Squad's Little Book of Pumping		978 184161 140 2	£2.50
The Odd Squad's Little Book of Sex		978 184161 095 5	£2.99
The Odd Squad's Little Book of Women		978 184161 094 8	£2.99
The Odd Squad's Little Book of X-Rated Cartoons		978 184161 141 9	£2.99

HOW TO ORDER: Please send a cheque/postal order in £ sterling, made payable to 'Ravette Publishing' for the cover price of the books and allow the following for post & packing ...

UK & BFPO -   70p for the first book & 40p per book thereafter
Europe & Eire -   £1.30 for the first book & 70p thereafter
Rest of the world - £2.20 for the first book & £1.10 per book thereafter

RAVETTE PUBLISHING
Unit 3, Tristar Centre, Star Road, Partridge Green, West Sussex RH13 8RA
tel: 01403 711443   *email*: ravettepub@aol.com

Prices and availability are subject to change without prior notice.